POWER CUT

PENCILS: JOHN MCCREA
INKS: LEE TOWNSEND
COLOURS: JAMES OFFREDI
SCRIPT: FERG HANDLEY

SO, IT'S SATURDAY AFTERNOON AND I'M ACTUALLY UP TO DATE WITH MY COLLEGE WORK. NO ASSIGNMENTS FOR THE DAILY BUGLE EITHER, MEANING I CAN GRAB SOME DOWN TIME. EXCEPT...

ANYHOW, THAT'S THE BOOTS I SAW EARLIER. AREN'T THEY TO DIE FOR?

TO YAWN FOR, MORE LIKE.

PETER, IF YOU DIDN'T WANT TO COME SHOPPING WITH ME, YOU SHOULD HAVE SAID SO ON THE PHONE.

YEAH, ABOUT THAT. YOUR EXACT WORDS WERE "HELP EMERGENCY. I NEED YOU TO MEET ME AT PENN STATION TIGER".

WHAT, SO YOU'D RATHER I JUST WALKED AROUND IN A PAIR OF OLD SNEAKERS? THANKS.

SEE, PROBLEM SOLVED. NOW CAN WE GO GET PIZZA?

OOH, MEN! THAT'S IT, NEXT TIME I'LL JUST ASK LIZ ALLEN INSTEAD!

COOL, JOB DONE.

I HEARD THAT, PARKER--

HOLD ON, MJ. SOMETHING'S HAPPENING OVER THERE...

Jewellery

KRASH

OUT OF MY WAY, YOU MISERABLE CRETINS!

DANG, IT'S THE VULTURE. WHICH MEANS I'D BETTER...

THIS IS BAD. NO SPIDER-SENSE, NO SUPER-STRENGTH, NO HEALING FACTOR... SO ALL I CAN DO IS TRY AND STAY OUT OF HIS REACH.

LUCKILY, I'VE STILL GOT MY WEBSHOOTERS...

FWIPP

...AND I'M REASONABLY FIT. BUT THEN AGAIN...

FWAAK

OH, HOW I'VE DREAMED OF THIS MOMENT. YOU, HELPLESS AND BEGGING FOR YOUR LIFE!

YEAH, LIKE *THAT'S* GONNA HAPPEN--

GIVE IT TIME, SPIDER-MAN, GIVE IT TIME!

HE'S RIGHT. NO WAY ON EARTH I CAN WIN HERE...

...SO I GUESS IT'S TIME TO SCRAM!!

KLUNK

HE CAN'T HAVE GONE FAR... SO WHERE IS HE, DRAT IT?

WELL, THAT DID IT. PROBLEM IS, WITHOUT MY SPIDEY-STRENGTH, I CAN'T GET AT MY CLOTHES UNTIL THE WEBBING DISSOLVES!

CONTINUED FROM PAGE 9

ANYWAY, I MAKE IT HOME, EVENTUALLY. AUNT MAY'S OFF VISITING A FRIEND FOR A FEW DAYS, WHICH IS HANDY -- BUT I FORGET TO LOCK THE FRONT DOOR AND...

PETER? WHERE DID YOU GET TO TODAY? I TRIED CALLING YOU, BUT...

I, ER, SLIPPED, MJ, AND FELL OFF A FIRE ESCAPE. IT'S OKAY THOUGH, NOTHING'S BROKEN...

OMIGOD! PETER, WHAT *HAPPENED* TO YOU?!

...BUT I DIDN'T GET ANY PHOTOS, SO SORRY ABOUT THAT.

OH YOU POOR THING. AND WHO CARES ABOUT THE PHOTOS, YOU COULD HAVE BROKEN YOUR NECK DOING THAT!

BLESS HER, SHE REALLY IS AN ANGEL. AND WHEN SHE'S GONE...

...I CAN'T HELP THINKING THAT MAYBE THIS IS FOR THE BEST. 'COS WITH NO POWERS, I CAN HAVE A NORMAL LIFE, LIKE ANY OTHER KID MY AGE.

DOESN'T LAST THOUGH. LIKE IT OR NOT, SPIDEY MAKES A DIFFERENCE IN THIS TOWN...

...AND BESIDES, THEY'RE MY POWERS, BLAST IT.

THE NEXT FEW DAYS ARE AGONY, AND I DON'T JUST MEAN THE BRUISES.

...YET ANOTHER JEWELLERY STORE ROBBED BY THE HIGH-FLYING VULTURE. STAY TUNED FOR MORE DETAILS, AFTER THIS WORD FROM OUR SPONSORS...

YEP, TOOMES IS RUNNING RIOT OUT THERE, MEANING I NEED TO GET BACK IN THE GAME SOMEHOW.

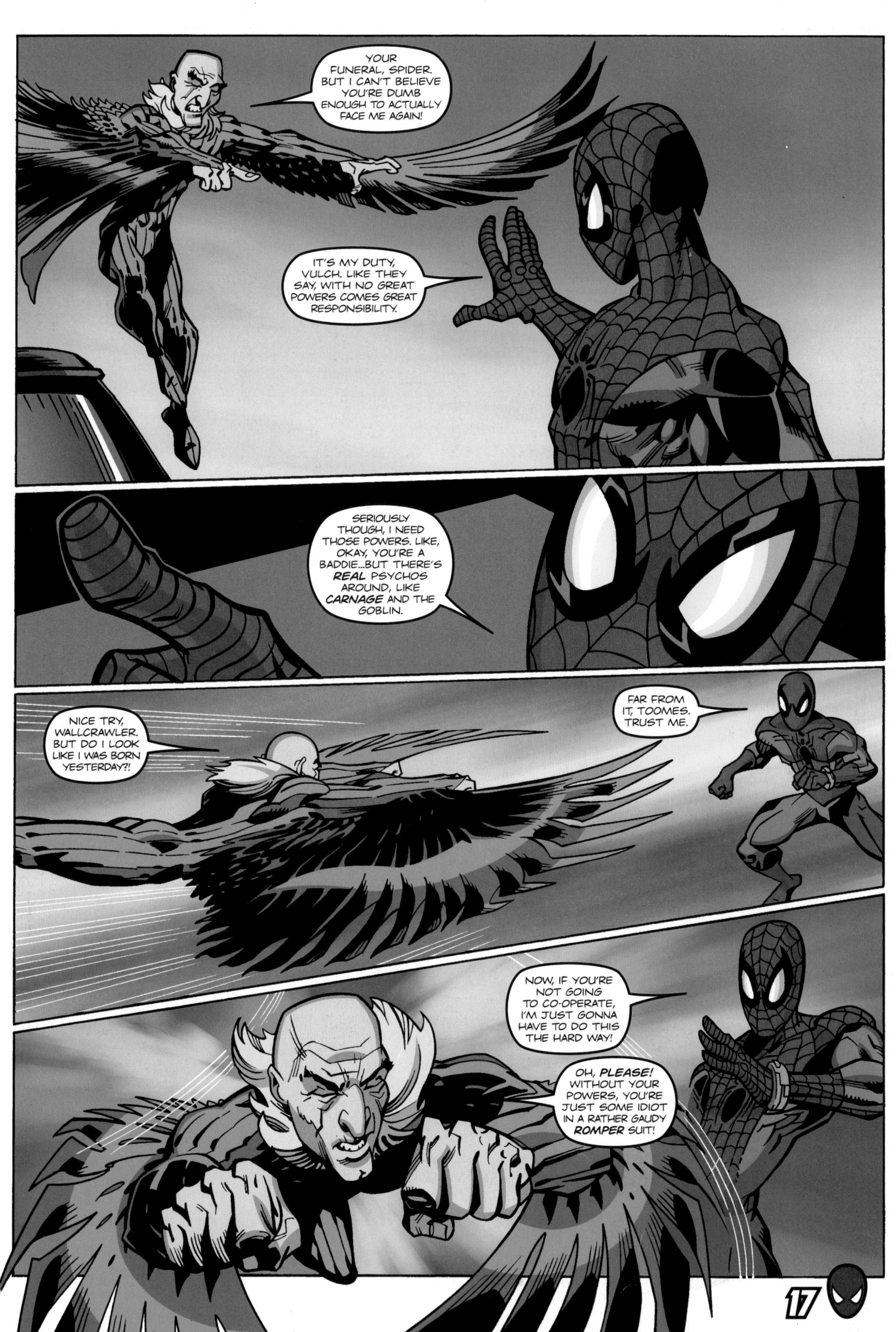

17

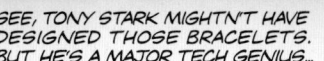

ESCAPE ROUTE!

SPIDEY

SPIDEY NEEDS TO GET BACK TO HIS CLOTHES, BUT CAN'T AFFORD TO RUN INTO VULTURE AGAIN WITHOUT HIS POWERS!

START

FINISH

CAN YOU FIND A ROUTE FROM SPIDEY TO HIS CLOTHES THAT AVOIDS ALL OF THE VULTURE'S HIDING PLACES?

CENTRAL!

CODE CRACKING!

REPLACE EACH LETTER WITH THE ONE BEFORE IT IN THE ALPHABET TO CRACK THE CODE!

LOOKS LIKE VULTURE DROPPED A SCRAP OF PAPER WITH THE NEXT PLACE HE'S ROBBING ON IT, BUT IT'S CODED!

TQBSLMFT KFXFMMFSZ TUPSF

....

....

DOUBLE VISION!

CAN YOU FIND ALL OF THE BIRD NAMES IN THE WORD GRID BELOW?

- FALCON
- HAWK
- EAGLE
- CUCKOO
- DOVE
- OWL
- PIGEON
- ROBIN
- PARROT
- PELICAN

S O H B L I T A C K E I N R
G A W A N I W J U R L L D E
N E O Z W F A L C O N C S A
D O V E G K Q S K I O N H G
P A L H M C K P O N T D Z L
T I S W P A R R O T I S V E
X S A T K E C B M U L C T I
W E K L B L N T N G O W P U
F O R T S O C W M I H S P U
U S E Q E T W Y R G P W L E Y
A U R G V A N L V O L E I U
Z O I S B J C T A W B L C D
W P M J A R I S V X T I A W
D S W C Y K S T O Z O W N K

SPIDER FILE

VULTURE'S NOT THE ONLY FLYING MARVELITE OUT THERE - CHECK OUT THESE OTHER...

WING III

ANGEL

POSSESSING POSSIBLY THE POSHEST CIVILIAN NAME OF ANY SUPER HERO, *WARREN WORTHINGTON III'S* LIFE CHANGED FOREVER WHEN WINGS STARTED TO SPROUT FROM HIS BACK.

WHEN A FIRE STRUCK HIS SCHOOL DORM, *WARREN* DISCOVERED THAT HIS WINGS ENABLED HIM TO FLY, AND WENT ABOUT SAVING AS MANY OF HIS SCHOOL FRIENDS AS HE COULD.

THIS SOON BROUGHT HIM TO THE ATTENTION OF *PROFESSOR CHARLES XAVIER*, WHO INVITED *WARREN* TO BECOME A FOUNDER MEMBER OF *THE X-MEN*, AS ANGEL.

THE WASP

WHEN AN ALIEN MONSTER KILLED *JANET VAN DYNE'S* SCIENTIST FATHER, SHE URGED HIS ASSOCIATE, *DR. HENRY PYM*, TO HELP HER AVENGE HIS DEATH.

OTHERWISE KNOWN AS *ANT-MAN*, PYM USED HIS *PYM PARTICLES* TO GRANT *JANET* THE ABILITY TO SHRINK, GROW WINGS, AND FIRE BLASTS OF ENERGY, BECOMING *THE WASP*.

ANT-MAN AND *THE WASP* MANAGED TO DEFEAT THE MONSTER, BEFORE GOING ON TO BECOME FOUNDING MEMBERS OF THE SUPER HERO GROUP, *THE AVENGERS*.

DRAGON MAN

ORIGINALLY CREATED BY *PROFESSOR GREGSON GILBERT* FOR STUDY AND RESEARCH, *DRAGON MAN* WAS BROUGHT TO LIFE BY A VILLAINOUS ALCHEMIST CALLED *DIABLO*.

DIABLO USED THE FIRE-BREATHING ANDROID TO ATTACK THE *FANTASTIC FOUR*, AND THIS WINGED BEAST HAS BEEN EXPLOITED BY EVIL DOERS EVER SINCE!

THE BEETLE

FED UP WITH HIS LOW PAYING MECHANIC'S JOB, *ABNER JENKINS* BUILT AN ARMOUR-PLATED, GRAVITY-DEFYING SUIT AND BECAME *THE BEETLE!*

HE USED HIS SUIT TO CHASE FAME, WEALTH AND POWER, BY COMMITTING A SERIES OF HIGH-PROFILE CRIMES, AND EVENTUALLY BEGAN TO OFFER HIS SERVICES TO GANGS LIKE THE MASTERS OF EVIL.

THE FALCON

SAM WILSON WAS ORIGINALLY GIVEN THE POWER TO TELEPATHICALLY COMMUNICATE WITH BIRDS BY *THE RED SKULL*, WHO USED THE COSMIC CUBE TO DO SO.

THE RED SKULL HOPED THAT *WILSON* WOULD HELP HIM DEFEAT *CAPTAIN AMERICA*, BUT INSTEAD, HE HELPED CAP DEFEAT *THE SKULL*, AND BECAME HIS CRIME-FIGHTING PARTNER.

NOW KNOWN AS *THE FALCON*, WILSON WAS ABLE TO REALLY LIVE UP TO HIS SUPER HERO NAME WHEN *THE BLACK PANTHER* CREATED A *WAKANDAN HARNESS* THAT ALLOWED HIM TO FLY.

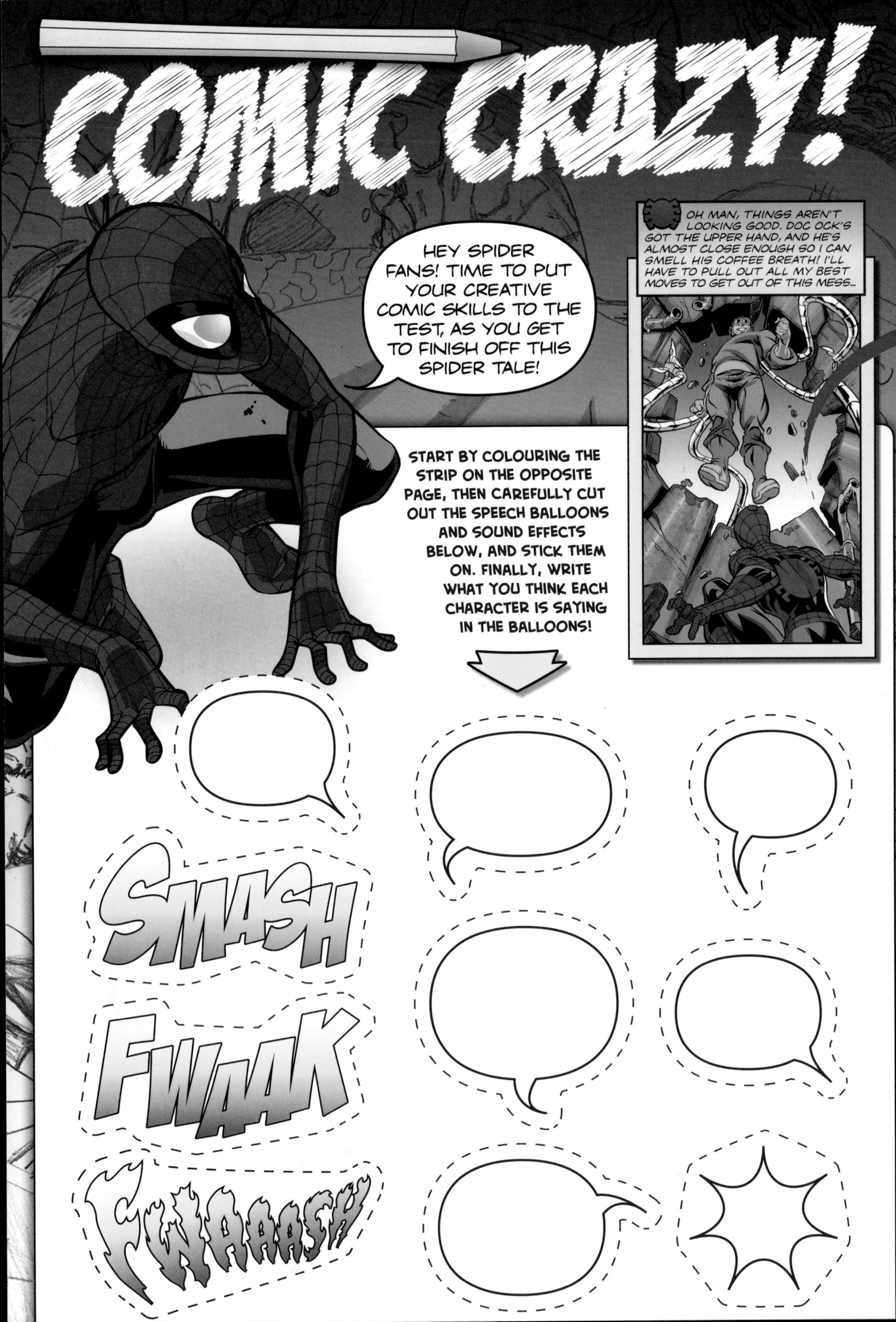

25

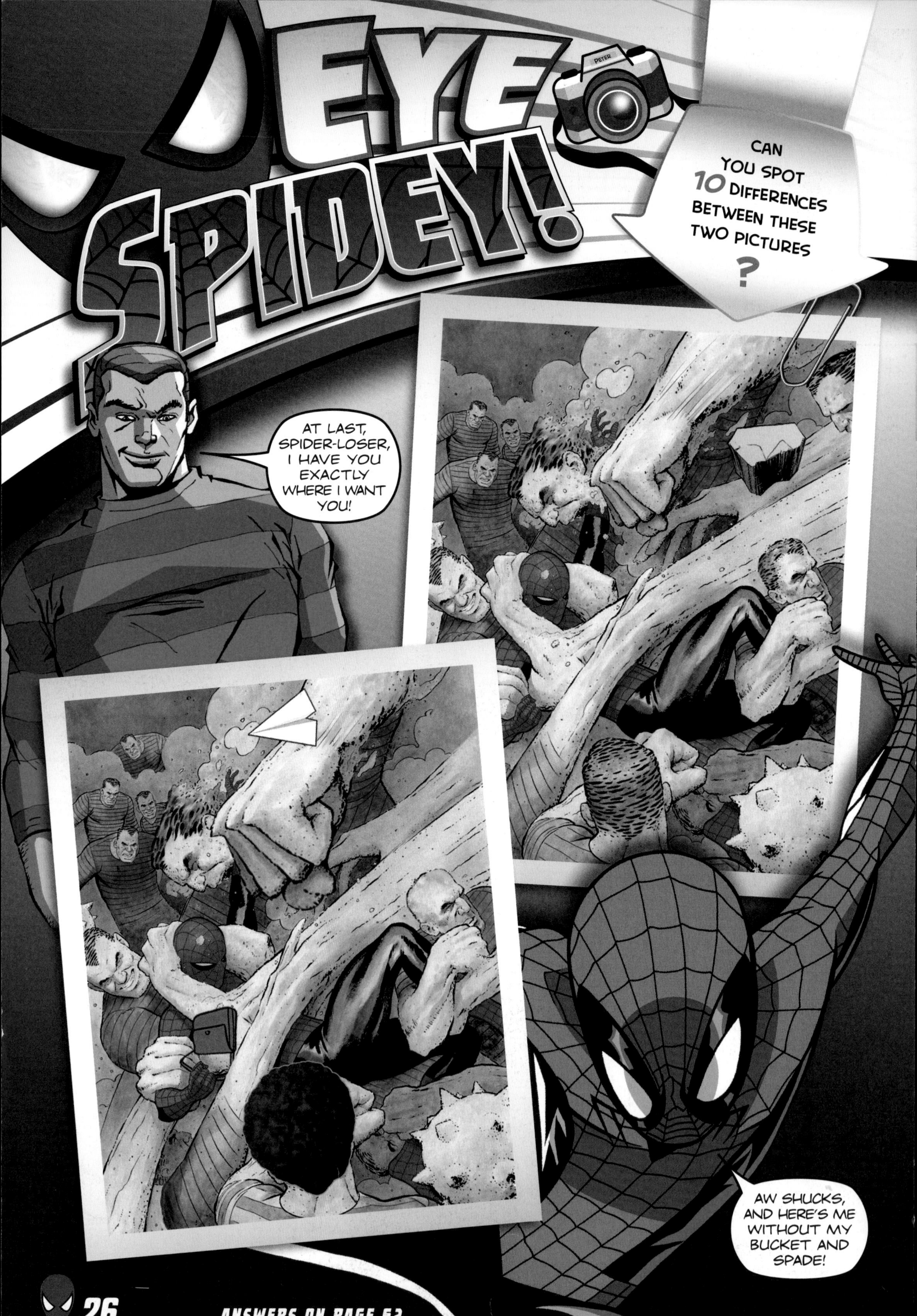

ANSWERS ON PAGE 62

HOO-BOY, THIS IS GONNA BE A DOOZY. WE'VE GOT THE HULK ON A MAJOR RAMPAGE, AND JUDGING BY THAT LAST NEWS FLASH, HE'S ALL OVER THE AVENGERS LIKE A RASH.

SO, WE'RE TALKING REAL POWERHOUSE STUFF HERE. AND I KNOW IT'S OUT OF MY LEAGUE, BUT I CAN MAYBE HELP PREVENT ANY CIVILIANS GETTING HURT IN THE...

...CROSSFIRE...!

PUNY HUMANS ANNOY HULK. SO HULK SMASH THEM ALL!

FORCE FIELD AT 18%

ALERT: SYSTEM FAILURE = IMMINENT

NOT GOOD. HULK'S BEING HULKY, AND IRON MAN'S THE LAST AVENGER STANDING...

33

SPIDER-FILE:

GOD OF THUNDER, LORD OF THE LIVING LIGHTNING, AND WIELDER OF THE MIGHTY HAMMER, MJOLNIR, READ ON TO FIND OUT MORE ABOUT THOR!

GOD SON

RAISED IN THE MYSTICAL KINGDOM OF *ASGARD*, THOR IS THE SON OF THE NORSE GOD, *ODIN*, AND GODDESS OF THE EARTH, *GAEA*.

ULTIMATE WARRIOR

BY THE AGE OF SIXTEEN, *THOR* HAD ALREADY GAINED A REPUTATION AS A MIGHTY WARRIOR, BUT HAD BECOME HEADSTRONG, PROUD AND SELFISH.

DOWN TO EARTH

TO TEACH HIS SON A LESSON IN HUMILITY, *ODIN* STRIPPED *THOR* OF HIS POWERS AND MEMORIES, AND SENT HIM TO EARTH, TO LIVE AS A CRIPPLED DOCTOR CALLED *DONALD BLAKE*.

LIFE LESSON

AS *BLAKE*, *THOR* BECAME THE HUMBLE AND PATIENT MAN HIS FATHER HAD HOPED HE WOULD, AND SO HIS TRUE IDENTITY WAS REVEALED TO HIM AGAIN.

THOR

DIVINE JUSTICE

NOW *THOR* SPLITS HIS TIME BETWEEN *ASGARD* AND THE MORTAL WORLD, USING HIS GOD-LIKE POWERS TO BRING JUSTICE TO BOTH.

LOKI

ADOPTED BY *ODIN* AFTER HIS FATHER DIED AT A YOUNG AGE, *LOKI* HAS ALWAYS BEEN INSANELY JEALOUS OF *THOR*.

HE REGULARLY USES ENERGY PROJECTION, HYPNOTISM AND ILLUSIONS TO TRICK PEOPLE INTO ATTACKING HIS FOSTER BROTHER, BUT IS STILL YET TO PERMANENTLY DEFEAT HIM.

BOTH HULK AND THOR ARE ABOUT AS STRONG AS THEY COME, BUT WHO IS THE STRONGEST BELOW?

ADD UP THE WEIGHT OF THE OBJECTS THEY ARE HOLDING TO WORK OUT WHO IS LIFTING MORE!

75 kg

750 kg

15 kg

950 kg

5 kg

10 kg

35 kg

125 kg

TOTAL WEIGHT

kg

TOTAL WEIGHT

kg

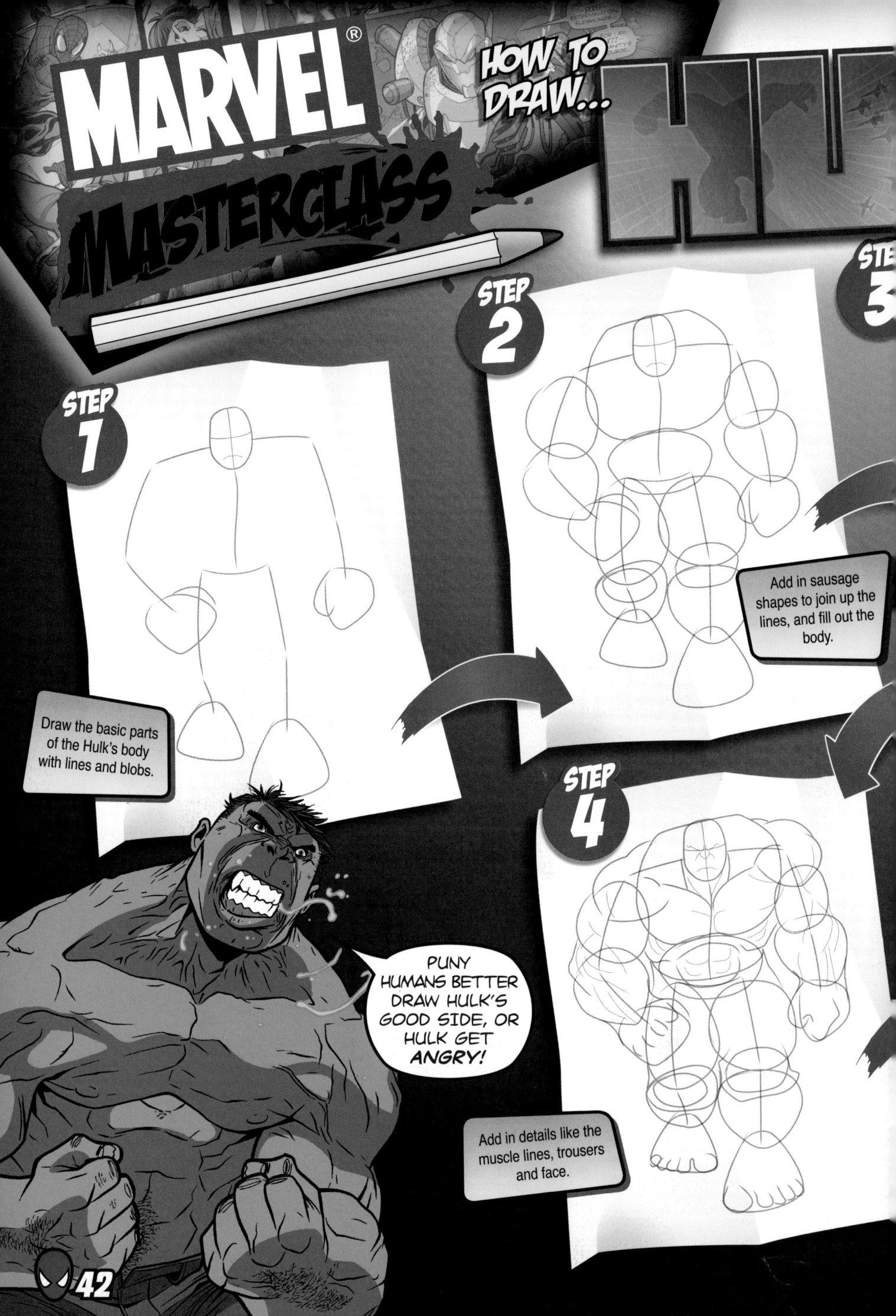

MARVEL® MASTERCLASS

HOW TO DRAW... HULK

STEP 1

Draw the basic parts of the Hulk's body with lines and blobs.

STEP 2

STEP 3

Add in sausage shapes to join up the lines, and fill out the body.

STEP 4

Add in details like the muscle lines, trousers and face.

PUNY HUMANS BETTER DRAW HULK'S GOOD SIDE, OR HULK GET ANGRY!

HEADS UP!

FOLLOW THESE STEPS TO DRAW **THE HULK'S** FACE AND HEAD!

1.
DRAW A ROUGH OVAL SHAPE, WITH VERY FAINT LINES RUNNING DOWN THE MIDDLE OF IT BOTH WAYS.

2.
DRAW THE EYES ALONG THE HORIZONTAL LINE, AND THE CENTRE OF THE NOSE AND MOUTH ON THE VERTICAL ONE.

3.
ADD A SLOPING BROW TO MAKE HULK LOOK ANGRY, AND A TUFT OF HAIR AND HIS TEETH.

Draw around the sausage shapes to form the outline of Hulk's body.

STEP 6

STEP 5

Go over your final picture with pen and rub the pencil out.

Finally, add some colour, using this picture as a guide!

43

MISTER FEAR MAY HAVE A FEW TRICKS UP HIS SLEEVE, BUT CHECK OUT THESE GUYS - YOU WON'T BELIEVE YOUR EYES!

MYSTERIO

5.

A master of make-up, stunts and hypnotism, *Mysterio* was a Hollywood special effects engineer, until he decided to take on *Spidey* with his illusion skills!

He developed a costume that pumped out hallucinogenic gas, which along with his carefully planned special effects, can make his enemies see terrifying images that aren't really there!

JACK O'LANTERN

He may look like a Halloween party reject, but *Jack O'Lantern* has an arsenal of pumpkin grenades ready to wipe out any hero who crosses him!

Mixed in with the usual smoke, explosive and concussion bombs are ones containing mind-altering fear gas, powerful enough to scare the pants off even the toughest of heroes!

3.

4. MISTER FEAR

This creepy customer is quite literally your worst nightmare! His costume is packed full of ways to emit his mind-altering fear gas, which does exactly what it says on the tin!

One whiff of his fearful pheromones and you'll be almost paralysed by the horrific hallucinations you see!

TOP 5
MASTERS OF

1. DOCTOR STRANGE

Taught by a reclusive shaman known as the Ancient One, *Dr. Steven Strange* is one of the most powerful sorcerers in existence.

He can use his magic to accomplish almost anything, including teleportation, dimensional travel, illusion-casting and thought projection – and you thought David Blaine was good!

MASTERMIND

No, this mutant's special ability isn't accelerated facial hair growth, it's actually illusion casting!

Mastermind can psionically cause others to see, hear, touch, smell and taste things which don't really exist. And it's not just limited to individuals either – he can make thousands of people see his illusions at the same time if he wishes!

2.

LUSION!

FRIGHT at the MUSEUM

SCRIPT: FERG HANDLEY PENCILS: JOHN ROYLE
INKS: GARY ERSKINE COLOURS: JAMES OFFREDI
LETTERING: ALEX FOOT

46

AAAAMPH!

NHGH!

WHOA, KINDA LOST IT A BIT THERE. BUT THAT'S THE THING ABOUT FEAR, IT'S LINKED TO ADRENALINE... AND IF YOU CAN'T RUN, CHANCES ARE, IT'LL MAKE YOU FIGHT.

...BUT FIRST...

STILL FREAKING OUT THOUGH. GOTTA GET OUT OF HERE...

FWIPP FWIPP

EYE SPIDEY!

CAN YOU SPOT 10 DIFFERENCES BETWEEN THESE TWO PICTURES?

ER, THIS ISN'T EXACTLY WHAT I HAD IN MIND WHEN YOU SAID YOU'D LIKE TO HAVE ME OVER FOR DINNER, LIZZY!

NONSENSSSE, SSSPIDER-MAN! I PROMISSSE THISSS WILL BE A MEAL YOU WILL NEVER FORGET!

ANSWERS ON PAGE 62

57

READ ON TO FIND OUT MORE ABOUT THE SUPER VILLAIN WHO HAS EVEN THE MIGHTIEST OF HEROES RUNNING FOR THEIR MUMMIES!

SCHOOL RIVAL

Larry Cranston hated Matt Murdock (AKA Daredevil) ever since he was humiliated by him in a mock trial at law school.

BE AFRAID...

To gain revenge on his nemesis, Cranston became Mister Fear, using his new costume's gruesome face and fear gas to scare the living daylights out of anyone who crossed him!

SMELL OF FEAR

Mister Fear's gas works by using pheromones to cause fear and panic in his victims, making them unable to fight, and distorting what they see into something more terrifying than Doc Ock in his underpants!

MISTER

TERROR ATTACK

Not only is Mister Fear scary, he's sneaky too! Check out the different ways he can make his enemies' blood run cold...

PUMP

Like a plug-in air freshener from hell, parts of *Mister Fear's* costume can emit fear gas without you noticing until it's too late!

TALONS

These are coated in a pheromone concentrate. If you're tagged with one of these, you're in for a fright-filled time!

GAS PELLETS

Shot from a gun, these rupture on impact, spreading enough fear gas to scare enemies stiff for up to 15 minutes!

DARTS

Fired from special gloves, these darts send a liquid form of pheromones directly into the bloodstream, for maximum terror!

FEAR

ANSWERS

EYE SPIDEY!

57

20 SPIDEY CENTRAL!

CODE CRACKING!
SPARKLES JEWELLERY STORE

DOUBLE VISION!

ESCAPE ROUTE!

60 SPIDEY CENTRAL!

TREBLE TERROR!
B

GREAT ESCAPE!

26 EYE SPIDEY!

IN THE SHADOWS!
A. Green Goblin; B. Doctor Doom;
C. Venom; D. Doc Ock

40 SPIDEY CENTRAL!

LIFT OFF!
HULK - 1060kg
THOR - 1055kg

DOUBLE VISION!

IRON MAN

CAPTAIN AMERICA

VISION

WASP

MISCHIEF MAKER!

A
B
C
D